BTEC First
Engineering

STUDY GUIDE

A PEARSON COMPANY

BTEC First Study Guide:
Engineering

Published by:Pearson Education Limited
Edinburgh Gate
Harlow
Essex CM20 2JE

First published 2008

Second Impression 2009

ISBN 978-1-84690-172-0

Printed by Ashford Colour Press Ltd, Gosport

Cover image © PunchStock: Digital Vision

The Publisher's policy is to use paper manufactured from sustainable forests.

All reasonable efforts have been made to trace and contact original copyright owners.

Contents

Preface

Following a BTEC programme is an exciting way to study. It gives you the opportunity to develop the knowledge, skills and understanding that you will need in the world of work.

BTECs are very different from GCSEs; a BTEC puts *you* in charge of your own learning. This guide has been written specially for you, to help you get started and succeed on your BTEC First course.

The **introduction**, Your BTEC First, tells you about your new course. This will be your companion through the BTEC First, as it:

- tells you how your BTEC will differ from GCSE;

- suggests how you can plan your time;

- explains ways to make the most of visits, guest speakers and work experience;

- advises you about resources and how to find information;

- gives you advice on making presentations and doing assignments.

The **activities** give you tasks to do on your own, in small groups or as a class. You will have the opportunity to put into practice the theory you learn. The activities will help you prepare for assessment by practising your skills and showing you how much you know. These activities are *not* intended for assessment.

The sample **marked assignments** (also sometimes called marked assessments) show you what other students have done to gain a Pass, Merit or Distinction. By seeing what past students have done, you should be able to improve your own grade.

Your BTEC First will cover either three or six units, depending on whether you are doing a Certificate or a Diploma. In this guide the activities cover sections from four units: Unit 1 'Working Practices in Engineering', Unit 2 'Using and Interpreting Engineering Information', Unit 3 'Applied Electrical and Mechanical Science for Technicians' and Unit 4 'Mathematics for Engineering Technicians'. These units underpin your study of engineering.

Because the guide covers only four units, it is important that you do all the other work your tutor sets you. Your tutor will ask you to research information in textbooks, in the library and on the internet. You may also have your own textbook for the course: use it! You should have the chance to visit local organisations or welcome guest speakers to your institution. This is a great way to find out more about your chosen vocational area – the type of jobs that are available and what the work is really like.

This guide is a taster, an introduction to your BTEC First. Use it as such, and make the most of the rich learning environment that your tutors will provide for you. Your BTEC First will give you an excellent base for further study, a broad understanding of engineering and the knowledge you need to succeed in the world of work.

Your BTEC First

Starting a new course is often both exciting and scary. It's normally exciting to do something new, and this includes learning different subjects that appeal to you. BTEC First courses are work-related, so you will be focusing on the work area that interests you. It can be nerve-wracking, though, if you are worried that there may be some topics that you will not understand, if you are unsure how you will be assessed, or if the prospect of some aspects of the course – such as finding out information on your own, or giving a presentation – makes your blood run cold!

It may help to know that these are worries common to many new BTEC First students. Yet every year thousands of them thoroughly enjoy their courses and successfully achieve the award.

Some do this the easy way, while others find it harder.

The easy way involves two things:

- knowing about the course and what you have to do

- positive thinking

Knowledge of the course means that you focus your time and energy on the things that matter. Positive thinking means that you aren't defeated before you start. Your ability to do well is affected by what goes on in your mind. A positive attitude helps you to meet new challenges more easily.

This guide has been written to give you all the information you need to get the most out of your course, to help you to develop positive thinking skills, and, of course, to help you successfully achieve your award. Keep it nearby throughout your course and re-read the relevant parts whenever you need to.

DO THINK	DON'T THINK
I'm quite capable of doing well on this course. First I need to check what I know about it and what I don't – and to fill in the gaps.	*If I struggle a bit or don't like something then so what? I can always drop out if I can't cope.*

Knowing about your course

If a friend or relative asked about your course, what would you say? Would you just shrug or give a vague comment? Or could you give a short, accurate description? If you can do this it usually means that you have a better understanding of what your course is all about – which means you are likely to be better prepared and better organised. You are also more likely to make links between your course and the world around you. This means you can be alert to information that relates to the subject you are studying.

→   Your family, friends, or other people you know may talk about topics that you are covering in class.

→   There may be programmes on television which relate to your studies.

→   Items in the news may be relevant.

→   You may work in a part-time job. Even if your part-time work is in a different area, there will still be useful links. For example, for most BTEC First courses you need to know how to relate to other people at work, how to assist your customers or clients and how to communicate properly. These are skills you need in most part-time jobs.

If you have only a hazy idea about your course then it is sensible to re-read any information you have been given by your school or college and to check further details on the Edexcel website at www.edexcel.org.uk. At the very least, you should know:

•   the type of BTEC award you are aiming for and how many units you will be taking:

◊   BTEC First Diploma – normally taken as a full-time course, with six units

◊   BTEC First Certificate – may be taken as a full-time or part-time course, with three units

•   the titles of your core units and what they cover

•   the number of specialist units you must take and the options available to you

Core units are compulsory for all students at all centres, and you can find details of them on the Edexcel website. The range of specialist units you can choose will depend upon which award you are taking and where you are studying. Many centres design their courses to meet the needs of the students in their area, in which case you won't have complete freedom to choose your own options. If you do have a choice, find out the content of each of the specialist units available, then think carefully about the ones you would most like to study. Then talk through your ideas with your tutor before you make a final decision.

<table>
<tr><th>DO THINK</th><th>DON'T THINK</th></tr>
<tr><td>The more I know about my course, the more I can link the different parts together and see how they relate to other areas of my life. This will give me a better understanding of the subjects I am studying.</td><td>It's unlikely that any course will have much relevance to my life or my interests, no matter what anyone says.</td></tr>
</table>

Knowing the difference: BTEC First versus GCSE

BTEC First awards are different from GCSEs in several ways. In addition to the differences in content, the way the topics are taught and the tutors' expectations of their students are also often different. Knowing about these gives you a better idea of what to expect – and how you should respond.

→ BTEC First awards are work-related. All the topics you learn relate to the skills and knowledge you will need in the workplace.

→ They are practical. You will learn how to apply your knowledge, both on your own and as a member of a team, to develop your skills and abilities.

→ Most full-time BTEC First Diploma courses in colleges are completed in one year. If you are taking a BTEC First Certificate course alongside your GCSEs, then you will probably be doing this over two years.

→ There are no exams. So you won't be expected to revise and learn lots of facts, or to write answers to questions in a hot exam room next June. Instead, you will complete assignments set by your tutors, based on learning outcomes set by Edexcel. You can read more about assignments on page 19, but for now you can think of them as being similar to coursework. They will be given to you through the year, and each will have a deadline. See page 19 for advice on coping with assignments, and page 9 for advice on managing your time effectively.

→ On a BTEC First course you will achieve Pass, Merit and Distinctions in your assignments. You will then be awarded an overall Pass, Merit or Distinction for the whole course.

→   BTEC First students are encouraged to take responsibility for their own learning. Your tutors won't expect to have to stand over you all the time to check what you are doing. This helps you to develop the skills to be mature and independent at work. You will be expected to be keen and interested enough to work hard without being continually monitored. You will also be expected to become more self-reliant and better organised as the course progresses. Some students thrive in this situation. They love having more freedom, and are keen to show that they can handle it, especially when they know that they can still ask for help or support when they need it. Other students – thankfully, a minority – aren't mature enough to cope in this situation, so it goes to their head and they run wild.

→   If you've just left school and are going to study for your BTEC First in a college, then you will find many other differences. No bells or uniforms! Maybe fewer timetabled hours; probably longer lesson periods. You will mix with a wider range of people, of different ages and nationalities. You are starting a whole new phase of your life, when you will meet new people and have new experiences. However strange it may seem at the beginning, new students normally settle down quickly. Even if they have been disappointed with some of their grades at GCSE, they are relieved that they can put this disappointment behind them and have a fresh start. If this applies to you, then it's up to you to make the most of it.

DO THINK	DON'T THINK
On my BTEC First course I can find out more about the area of work that interests me. I will enjoy proving that I can work just as well with less direct supervision, and know I can get help and support when I need it.	*Doing a BTEC First will be great because the tutors won't be breathing down my neck all the time and won't care if I mess around on the course.*

Knowing how to use your time

How well organised are you? Do you always plan in advance, find what you've put away, and remember what you've promised to do without being reminded? Or do you live for the moment – and never know what you will be doing more than six hours in advance? Would you forget who you were, some days, unless someone reminded you?

School teachers cope with young students like this by giving homework on set nights, setting close deadlines, and regularly reminding everyone when work is due. They don't (or daren't!) ask students to do something over the next couple of months and then just leave them to it.

Although your BTEC First tutor will give you reminders, he or she will also be preparing you for higher-level courses and for having a responsible job – when you will be expected to cope with a range of tasks and deadlines with few, if any, reminders. On your BTEC First course some work will need to be completed quickly and done for the next session. But other tasks may take some time to do – such as finding out information on a topic, or preparing a presentation. You may be set tasks like this several weeks in advance of the deadline, and it can be easy to put them off, or to forget them altogether – with the result that you may not do the task at all, or end up doing a sloppy job at the last minute because you haven't had time to do it properly.

This problem gets worse over time. At the start of a new course there always seems to be a lot of time and not much pressure: the major deadlines may seem far in the future, and you may find it easy to cope day by day.

This situation is unlikely to last. Some tasks may take you longer than you had thought. Several tutors may want work completed at the same time. And deadlines have a nasty habit of speeding up as they approach. If you have lots of personal commitments too, then you may struggle to cope, and get very stressed or be tempted to give up.

The best way to cope is to learn to manage your own time, rather than letting it manage you. The following tips may help.

→ Expect to have work to do at home, both during the week and at weekends, and plan time for this around your other commitments. It's unrealistic to think that you can complete the course without doing much at home.

→ Schedule fixed working times into your week, taking your other commitments into account. For example, if you always play five-a-side football on Monday evening, keep Tuesday evening free for catching up with work. Similarly, if you work every Saturday, keep some time free on Sunday for work you have to complete over the weekend.

→ Get into the habit of working at certain times, and tell other people in your life what you are doing. If you've no work to do on one of these days, then that's a bonus. It's always easier to find something to do when you unexpectedly have free time than to find time for a task you didn't expect.

→ Write down exactly what you have to do in a diary or notebook the moment you are told about it, so that you don't waste time doing the wrong thing – or ringing lots of people to find out if they know what it is you're supposed to be doing.

→ Normally you should do tasks in order of urgency – even if this means you can't start with the one you like the best. But if, for example, you need to send off for information and wait for it to arrive, you can use the time to work on less urgent tasks.

→ Don't forget to include in your schedule tasks that have to be done over a period of time. It's easy to forget these if you have lots of shorter deadlines to meet. Decide how long the whole task is likely to take you, break the total time up into manageable chunks, and allocate enough time to complete it by the deadline date.

→ Always allow more time than you think you will need, never less.

→ Be disciplined! Anyone who wants to get on in life has to learn that there are times when you have to work, even if you don't want to. Try rewarding yourself with a treat afterwards.

→ If you are struggling to motivate yourself, set yourself a shorter time limit and really focus on what you are doing to get the most out of the session. You may be so engrossed when the time is up that you want to carry on.

→ Speak to your tutor promptly if you have a clash of commitments or a personal problem that is causing you serious difficulties – or if you have truly forgotten an important deadline (then vow not to do so again)!

→ If few of these comments apply to you because you are well organised, hard-working and regularly burn the midnight oil trying to get everything right, then don't forget to build leisure time and relaxation into your schedule. And talk to your tutor if you find that you are getting stressed out because you are trying too hard to be perfect.

DO THINK	DON'T THINK
I am quite capable of planning and scheduling the work I have to do, and being self-disciplined about doing it. I don't need a tutor to do this for me.	*I can only work when I'm in the mood and it's up to my tutors to remind me what to do and when.*

Knowing about resources

Resources for your course include the handouts you are given by your tutor, the equipment and facilities at your school or college (such as the library and resource centre), and information you can obtain on the internet from websites that relate to your studies. Resources that are essential for your course – such as a computer and access to the internet – will always be provided. The same applies to specialist resources required for a particular subject. Other resources – such as paper, file folders and a pen – you will be expected to provide yourself.

→ Some popular (or expensive) resources may be shared, and may need to be reserved in advance. These may include popular textbooks in the library, and laptop computers for home use. If it's important to reserve this resource for a certain time, don't leave it till the last minute.

→ You can only benefit from a resource if you know how to use it properly. This applies, for example, to finding information in the library, or using PowerPoint to prepare a presentation. Always ask for help if you need it.

→ You cannot expect to work well if you are forever borrowing what you need. Check out the stationery and equipment you need to buy yourself, and do so before the course starts. Many stationers have discounts on stationery near the start of term.

→ Look after your resources, to avoid last-minute panics or crises. For example, file handouts promptly and in the right place, follow the guidelines for using your IT system, and replace items that are lost or have ceased to work.

DO THINK	DON'T THINK
I have all the resources I need for my course, and I know how to use them or how to find out.	*I can find out what's available if and when I need it, and I can always cadge stuff from someone else.*

Knowing how to get the most from work experience

On some BTEC First courses – such as Children's Care, Learning and Development – all students must undertake a related work placement. On others, work placements are recommended but not essential, or may be required only for some specialist units. So whether or not you spend time on work experience will depend upon several factors, including the course you are taking, the units you are studying, and the opportunities in your own area. You will need to check with your tutor to find out whether you will be going on a work placement as part of your course.

If you need evidence from a work placement for a particular unit, then your tutor will give you a log book or work diary, and will help you to prepare for the experience. You should also do your best to help yourself.

Your placement

→   Check you have all the information about the placement you need, such as the address, start time, and name of your placement supervisor.

→   Know the route from home and how long it will take you to get there.

→   Know what is suitable to wear, and what is not – and make sure all aspects of your appearance are appropriate to your job role.

→   Know any rules, regulations or guidelines that you must follow.

→   Check you know what to do if you have a problem during the placement, such as being too ill to go to work.

→   Talk to your tutor if you have any special personal worries or concerns.

→   Understand why you are going on the placement and how it relates to your course.

→   Know the units to which your evidence will apply.

→   Check the assessment criteria for the units and list the information and evidence you will need to obtain.

DO THINK	DON'T THINK
Work experience gives me the opportunity to find out more about possible future workplaces, and link my course to reality.	*Work experience just means I'll be given all the boring jobs to do.*

Knowing how to get the most from special events

BTEC First courses usually include several practical activities and special events. These make the work more interesting and varied, and give you the opportunity to find out information and develop your skills and knowledge in new situations. They may include visits to external venues, visits from specialist speakers, and team events.

Some students enjoy the chance to do something different, while others can't see the point. It will depend on whether or not you are prepared to take an active involvement in what is happening. You will normally obtain the most benefit if you make a few preparations beforehand.

→   Listen carefully when any visit outside school or college, or any arrangement for someone to visit you, is being described. Check you understand exactly why this has been organised and how it relates to your course.

→   Find out what you are expected to do, and any rules or guidelines you must follow, including any specific requirements related to your clothes or appearance.

→   Write down all the key details, such as the date, time, location, and names of those involved. Always allow ample time so that you arrive five minutes early for any special event, and are never late.

→   Your behaviour should be impeccable whenever you are on a visit or listening to a visiting speaker.

→ Check the information you will be expected to prepare or obtain. Often this will relate to a particular assignment, or help you understand a particular topic in more detail.

→ For an external visit, you may be expected to write an account of what you see or do, or to use what you learn to answer questions in an assignment. Remember to take a notebook and pen with you, so that you can make notes easily.

→ For an external speaker, you may be expected to prepare a list of questions as well as to make notes during the talk. Someone will also need to say 'thank you' afterwards on behalf of the group. If your class wants to tape the talk, it's polite to ask the speaker for permission first.

→ For a team event, you may be involved in planning and helping to allocate different team roles. You will be expected to participate positively in any discussions, to talk for some (but not all) of the time, and perhaps to volunteer for some jobs yourself.

→ Write up any notes you make during the event neatly as soon as possible afterwards – while you can still understand what you wrote!

DO THINK	DON'T THINK
I will get more out of external visits, visiting speakers and team events if I prepare in advance, and this will also help me to get good grades.	*Trips out and other events are just a good excuse to have a break and take it easy for bit.*

Knowing how to find out information

Many students who are asked to find out information find it difficult to do so effectively. If they are online, they often print out too much, or can't find what they want. Similarly, too many students drift aimlessly around a library rather than purposefully search for what they need.

Finding out information is a skill that you need to learn. You need to know where to look, how to recognise appropriate information, and when to stop looking in order to meet your deadline, as well as what to do with the information when you've found it.

The first thing to realise is that you will never be asked to find out information for no reason. Before you start, you need to know what you are looking for, why it is needed, where you can find it, and the deadline.

This means you target your search properly and start looking in the right place.

Researching in the library

→   Find out the order in which books are stored. This is normally explained to all students during their induction.

→   Know the other resources and facilities that are available in your library besides books – for example, CD-ROMs and journals.

→   Take enough change with you so that you can photocopy articles that you can't remove. Remember to write down the source of any article you photocopy.

→   If you need specific books or articles, and aren't sure where they will be, try to visit during a quiet time, when the librarian can give you help if you need it.

→   If you find two or three books which include the information you need, that's normally enough. Too many can be confusing.

→   Check quickly if a book contains the information you need by looking in the index for the key words and then checking you can understand the text. If you can't, then forget it and choose another. A book is only helpful to you if you can follow it.

Researching online

→   Use a good search engine to find relevant websites. Scroll down the first few pages of the search results and read the descriptions to see which sites seem to be the best.

→   Remember to read all parts of the screen to check what's available on a website, as menus may be at the foot of the page as well as at the top or on either side. Many large sites have a search facility or a site map which you can access if you are stuck.

→   Don't get distracted by irrelevant information. If your searches regularly lead nowhere, ask your IT resource staff for help.

→   Don't print out everything you read. Even if printouts are free, too much information is just confusing.

→   Bookmark sites you use regularly and find helpful.

Researching by asking other people

This doesn't mean asking someone else to do the work for you! It means finding out about a topic by asking an expert.

→ Think about the people you know who might be able to help you because they have knowledge or experience that would be useful.

→ Prepare in advance by thinking about the best questions to ask.

→ Then contact the person and (unless you know the person well) introduce yourself.

→ Explain politely and clearly why you need the information.

→ Ask your questions, but don't gabble or ask them too quickly.

→ Write notes, so that you don't forget what you are told. Put the name and title of the person, and the date, at the top of the first page.

→ Ask if you can contact the person again, in case there is anything you need to check. Write down their phone number or email address.

→ Remember to say 'thank you'.

Using your information

→ Keep all your information on a topic neatly in a labelled folder or file. If you think you might want to reuse the folder later, put the title on in pencil rather than ink.

→ Refresh your memory of the task by re-reading it before you start to sift the information. Then only select pages that are relevant to the question you have been asked. Put all the other paper away.

→ Remember that you will rarely just be asked to reproduce the information that you have obtained. You will need to make decisions about which parts are the most relevant and how you should use these. For example, if you have visited a sports facility to find out what is available, then you may have to explain which activities are targeted at certain groups of people. You would be expected to disregard information that didn't relate to that task. Or you may be asked to evaluate the facilities, in which case you would have to consider how well the centre met the needs of its users and how it could do better.

→ Never rewrite copied information and pretend they are your own words! This is plagiarism, which is a serious offence with severe penalties. You need to state the source of your material by including the name of the author or the web address – either in the text, or as part of a list at the end. Your tutor will show you how to do this if you are not sure.

→ Write a draft and then ask your tutor to confirm that you are on the right track. You can also check with your tutor if you are unsure whether or not to include certain types of information.

DO THINK	DON'T THINK
Researching can be fun, and practice makes perfect. If I'm struggling to find something or to know what to include, I'll ask for help. Then it will be easier next time.	*The more I find the better, because collecting or writing a lot always impresses people.*

Knowing how to make a presentation

Presentations are a common feature of many BTEC courses. Usually you will be asked to do a presentation as a member of a team. If the team works together and its members support each other then this is far less of an ordeal than it may first seem. The benefits are that you learn many skills, including how to be a team member, how to speak in public, and how to prepare visual aids (often using PowerPoint) – all of which are invaluable for your future career.

Many students get worried about the idea of standing up to speak in front of an audience. This is quite normal, and can even improve your performance if you know how to focus your anxieties productively!

Presentation tasks can be divided into three stages: the initial preparations, the organisation, and the delivery.

Preparation

→   Divide up the work of researching fairly among the team.

→   Bear in mind people's individual strengths and weaknesses and allow for these, so that you all gain from working as a team.

→   Work out how long each person must speak so that you don't exceed your time limit (either individually or as a team).

→   Agree on the type of visual aids that would be best, given your topic. Keeping things simple is often more effective than producing something elaborate that doesn't work properly.

→   Decide on any handouts that are required, prepare these and check them carefully.

→   Check you know when and where the presentation will be held and what you should wear.

→ Think in advance about any questions you may be asked, both individually and as a team.

Organisation

→ Decide who will start and how each person will be introduced. Sometimes the lead person introduces everyone; on other occasions people introduce themselves.

→ Decide the most logical order in which to speak, bearing in mind everyone's contribution and how it fits into the overall presentation.

→ Prepare prompt cards. It's easy to forget some of the things you want to say, so put your main points down in the right order on a prompt card. Never read from this! Instead, write clearly and neatly so that you can just glance down to check on your next point.

→ Check you have sufficient copies of any handouts, and that these are clear and easy to read.

→ Rehearse several times and check your timings.

→ Get your clothes ready the night before.

→ Arrive at the event in plenty of time so that you're not in a rush.

Delivery

→ Take a few deep breaths before you start, to calm your nerves.

→ Make eye contact with your audience, and smile.

→ Keep your head up.

→ Speak a little more slowly than usual.

→ Speak a little more loudly than usual – without shouting.

→ Answer any questions you are asked. If you don't know the answer, be honest – don't guess or waffle.

→ Offer to help a team member who is struggling to answer a question, if you know the answer.

DO THINK	DON'T THINK
If I am well prepared and organised then my presentation will be OK, even if I'm really scared. The audience will always make allowances for some nerves.	*I'm confident about speaking in public so I don't have to bother preparing in advance.*

Knowing the importance of assignments

All BTEC First students are assessed by means of assignments. Each assignment is designed to link to specific learning outcomes. Assignments let you demonstrate that you have the skills and knowledge to get a Pass, Merit or Distinction grade. At the end of your course, your assignment grades together determine the overall grade for your BTEC First Certificate or Diploma.

Each assignment you are given will comprise specific tasks. Many will involve you in obtaining information (see page 14) and then applying your new-found knowledge to produce a written piece of work. Alternatively, you may demonstrate your knowledge by giving a presentation or taking part in an activity.

To get a good grade, you must be able to produce a good response to assignments. To do so, you need to know the golden rules that apply to all assignments, then how to interpret your instructions to get the best grade you can.

The golden rules for assignments

→   Read your instructions carefully. Check that you understand everything, and ask your tutor for help if there is anything that puzzles or worries you.

→   Check that you know whether you have to do all the work on your own, or if you will have to do some as a member of a group. If you work as a team, you will always have to identify which parts are your own contribution.

→   Write down any verbal instructions you are given, including when your tutor is available to discuss your research or any drafts you have prepared.

→ Check you know the date of the final deadline and any penalties for not meeting this.

→ Make sure you know what to do if you have a serious personal problem and need an official extension. An example would be if you were ill and expected to be absent for some time.

→ Remember that copying someone else's work (plagiarism) is always a serious offence – and is easy for experienced tutors to spot. Your school or college will have strict rules which state the consequences of doing this. It is never worth the risk.

→ Schedule enough time for finding out the information and making your initial preparations – from planning a presentation to writing your first draft or preparing an activity.

→ Allow plenty of time between talking to your tutor about your plans, preparations and drafts and the final deadline.

Interpreting your instructions to get the best grade you can

→ Most assignments start with a command word – for example, 'describe', 'explain' or 'evaluate'. These words relate to the level of answer required. A higher level of response is required for a Merit grade than for a Pass, and a higher level still for a Distinction.

→ Students often fall short in an assignment because they do not realise the differences between these words and what they have to do in each case. The tables below show you what is usually required for each grade when you see a particular command word.

→ As you can see from the tables, to obtain a higher grade with a given command word (such as 'describe'), you usually need to give a more complex description or use your information in a different way. You can refer to the example answers to real assignments, and tutor comments, from page 57 onwards.

→ You can check the command words you are likely to see for each unit in the grading grid. It is sensible to read this carefully in advance, so that you know the evidence that you will have to present to obtain a Pass, Merit or Distinction grade.

→ Be prepared to amend, redraft or rethink your work following feedback from your tutor, so that you always produce work that you know is your best effort.

→ Learn how to record your achievement so that you can see your predicted overall grade. Your tutor will show you how to do this, using the Edexcel *Recording your Achievement* form for your subject.

The following tables show what is required to obtain a Pass, Merit and Distinction, for a range of different 'command words'. Generally speaking:

- To obtain a Pass grade, you must be able to show that you understand the key facts relating to a topic.

- To obtain a Merit grade, you must be able to show that, in addition to fulfilling the requirements for a Pass grade, you can also use your knowledge in a certain way.

- To obtain a Distinction grade, you must be able to show that, in addition to fulfilling the requirements for a Pass and a Merit grade, you can also apply your knowledge to a situation and give a reasoned opinion.

Obtaining a Pass

Complete...	Complete a form, diagram or drawing.
Demonstrate...	Show that you can do a particular activity.
Describe...	Give a clear, straightforward description which includes all the main points.
Identify...	Give all the basic facts which relate to a certain topic.
List...	Write a list of the main items (not sentences).
Name...	State the proper terms related to a drawing or diagram.
Outline...	Give all the main points, but without going into too much detail.
State...	Point out or list the main features.

Examples:

- *List the main features on your mobile phone.*

- *Describe the best way to greet a customer.*

- *Outline the procedures you follow to keep your computer system secure.*

Obtaining a Merit

Analyse...	Identify the factors that apply, and state how these are linked and how each of them relates to the topic.
Comment on...	Give your own opinions or views.
Compare... Contrast...	Identify the main factors relating to two or more items and point out the similarities and differences.
Competently use...	Take full account of information and feedback you have obtained to review or improve an activity.
Demonstrate...	Prove you can carry out a more complex activity.
Describe...	Give a full description including details of all the relevant features.
Explain...	Give logical reasons to support your views.
Justify...	Give reasons for the points you are making so that the reader knows what you are thinking.
Suggest...	Give your own ideas or thoughts.

Examples:

- *Explain why mobile phones are so popular.*

- *Describe the needs of four different types of customers.*

- *Suggest the type of procedures a business would need to introduce to keep its IT system secure.*

Obtaining a Distinction

Analyse...	Identify several relevant factors, show how they are linked, and explain the importance of each.
Compare... Contrast...	Identify the main factors in two or more situations, then explain the similarities and differences, and in some cases say which is best and why.
Demonstrate...	Prove that you can carry out a complex activity taking into account information you have obtained or received to adapt your original ideas.

Describe...	Give a comprehensive description which tells a story to the reader and shows that you can apply your knowledge and information correctly.
Evaluate...	Bring together all your information and make a judgement on the importance or success of something.
Explain...	Provide full details and reasons to support the arguments you are making.
Justify...	Give full reasons or evidence to support your opinion.
Recommend...	Weigh up all the evidence to come to a conclusion, with reasons, about what would be best.

Examples:

- *Evaluate the features and performance of your mobile phone.*

- *Analyse the role of customer service in contributing to an organisation's success.*

- *Justify the main features on the website of a large, successful organisation of your choice.*

DO THINK	DON'T THINK
Assignments give me the opportunity to demonstrate what I've learned. If I work steadily, take note of the feedback I get and ask for advice when I need it, there is no reason why I can't get a good grade.	*If I mess up a few assignments it isn't the end of the world. All teachers like to criticise stuff, and I only wanted a Pass anyway.*

Knowing what to do if you have a problem

If you are lucky, you will sail through your BTEC First with no major problems. Unfortunately, not every student is so lucky. Some may encounter personal difficulties or other issues that can seriously disrupt their work. If this happens to you, it's vitally important that you know what to do.

→ Check that you know who to talk to if you have a problem. Then check who you should see if that person happens to be away at the time.

→ Don't sit on a problem and worry about it. Talk to someone, in confidence, promptly.

→ Most schools and colleges have professional counselling staff you can see if you have a concern that you don't want to tell your tutor. They will never repeat anything you say to them without your permission.

→ If you have a serious complaint, it's a good idea to talk it over with one of your tutors before you do anything else. Schools and colleges have official procedures to cover important issues such as appeals about assignments and formal complaints, but it's usually sensible to try to resolve a problem informally first.

→ If your school or college has a serious complaint about you, it is likely to invoke its formal disciplinary procedures, and you should know what these are. If you have done something wrong or silly, remember that most people will have more respect for you if you are honest about it, admit where you went wrong and apologise promptly. Lying only makes matters worse.

→ Most students underestimate the ability of their tutors to help them in a crisis – and it's always easier to cope with a worry if you've shared it with someone.

DO THINK	DON'T THINK
My tutors are just as keen for me to do well as I am, and will do everything they can to help me if I have a problem.	*No one will believe I have a problem. Tutors just think it's an excuse to get out of working.*

Finally...

This introduction wasn't written just to give you another task to do! It was written to help you to do your best and get the most out of your course.

So don't just put it on one side and forget about it. Go back to it from time to time to remind yourself about how to approach your course. You may also find it helpful to show it to other people at home, so that they will understand more about your course and what you have to do.

Activities

1   Working Practices in Engineering

This section provides an introduction to Unit 1, and covers the grading criteria P1, P2, P3, M1 and D1.

Unit abstract for these criteria

The ability to work safely in an engineering environment is essential for the well-being of self and others. The aim of this unit is to deal with the essential working practices of engineering to ensure that you appreciate potential hazards. This way, you can enjoy all the challenges that an engineering profession can offer without undue fear for your own safety or for that of others.

The unit starts by considering how materials and equipment should be handled and the most appropriate personal protective equipment (for example, eye or hand protection) to use when undertaking particular engineering activities. You will examine the hazards and risks associated with an engineering activity, including the working environment (for example, working at height), the use of tools and equipment, and working with materials and substances that may cause harm. A key focus of the unit is acquiring an awareness of the dangers of not working within appropriate legislation and procedures. In the event of an incident it is essential that you know how to respond. The unit will take you through typical incidents that you may have to deal with at some point in your career (for example, contacting the first aider, sounding alarms, stopping machinery).

Learning outcomes

On completion of this unit you should:
1 Understand statutory regulations and organisational safety requirements
2 Be able to work efficiently and effectively in engineering

Unit content (for critera P1, P2, P3, M1 and D1)

Materials and equipment handling: own and others' roles and responsibilities eg under the Health and Safety at Work Act and other current and relevant legislation applicable to the working environment, management of health and safety at work regulations, workplace health, safety and welfare regulations, personal and protective equipment at work regulations, manual handling operations regulations; identification of warning signs for the seven main groups of hazardous substances eg defined by classification, packaging and labelling of dangerous substances regulations; sources of information and guidance within an organisation; using equipment safely eg mechanical, electrical, fluid power equipment; lifting and carrying techniques; housekeeping eg tidy workspace, protecting others from harm eg as a result of work being carried out by self or others.

Personal protective equipment (PPE): appropriate to task undertaken eg overalls, protective footwear, eye protection, masks/respirators.

Hazards and risks: working environment eg working at height, in confined spaces, hot work; tools and equipment used; materials and substances used; dangers of not working to laid-down procedures.

Emergency procedures: engineering workshop incidents (accident/injury, work hazards, fire); identification of appropriate qualified persons eg first aider, fire warden; actions in the event of an accident or emergency eg use of fire extinguishers (types and applications), types and sounding/initiating emergency alarm, evacuation procedure and escape routes; reporting routines eg at assembly point, hazards and malfunctions, injury, near-miss occurrences.

Engineering work activity: prepare work environment eg area free from hazards, safety procedures implemented, PPE and tools obtained and checked (safe and usable condition); prepare for activity eg all necessary drawings, specifications, job instructions, materials/components obtained, storage arrangements for work, authorisation to carry out work; complete work activity eg complete all tasks and documentation, return drawings/work instructions and tools, dispose of unusable tools, equipment, components and waste materials (oil, soiled rags, swarf/off cuts).

A brief explanation of what you need to do for the grading criteria covered in this guide is given in the following table:

Grading criteria	What do I need to do for this?
P1 handle materials and equipment in an engineering workplace in a safe and approved manner	You will need to show that you follow basic safety procedures when carrying materials, such as heavy objects. Also you need to demonstrate that you can handle mechanical and/or electrical equipment in a safe way. This work needs to be done in a practical way, so it will involve witness statements from your teacher. Finally you should be able to identify the seven main groups of hazardous substance from their labels or warning signs.
P2 select and use appropriate personal protective equipment when undertaking a given engineering activity	You will need to show that you can select the appropriate personal protective equipment (PPE), such as safety goggles, rubber gloves or protective footwear, for a task such as using an electric drill.
P3 identify hazards and risks associated with an engineering activity	You need to know other risks, such as working at height, and the hazards involved in drilling or not following safety procedures.
M1 carry out a risk assessment on an engineering workplace to make recommendations on the safety of materials and equipment handling, use of personal protective equipment and the potential hazards in the area	A school or college workshop could be used for this. Or, if you have access to some other engineering workplace, that also would be OK. The risk could come from using hand tools, power tools, or from equipment left lying around on the floor. Three or four risks would be enough.
D1 prepare a safety policy for an engineering work area including references to relevant legislation	The same area as for "M1" can be used. For this area a safety policy, with references, is needed.

The Health and Safety at Work Act 1974

This is one of the most important safety laws – it places duties on both the employer and employee to make sure that workplaces are as safe as possible.

Even with this law, which gets regularly updated, there are over 200,000 work injuries in the UK each year and over 200 deaths.

This shows how important it is to make sure that you always place safety at the top of the list when carrying out any engineering work.

The outlines of this law, taken from the HSE (Health and Safety Executive) website, are as follows:

You have the right:
- To work in places where all the risks to your health and safety are properly controlled.
- To stop working and leave the area if you think you are in danger.
- To inform your employer about health and safety issues or concerns.
- To contact HSE or your local authority if you still have health and safety concerns and not get into trouble.
- To join a trade union and be a safety representative.
- To paid time off work for training if you are a safety representative.
- To a rest break of at least 20 minutes if you work more than six hours at a stretch and to an annual period of paid leave.

You must:
- Take care of your own health and safety and that of people who may be affected by what you do (or do not do).
- Co-operate with others on health and safety, and not interfere with, or misuse, anything provided for your health, safety or welfare.

Note that these last two points refer to your responsibility not only for your own safety, but also for other people in your work area.

Activity 1: Lifting and carrying (P1)

Lifting or carrying heavy loads can cause injuries to the back, and needs to be done with care. You may already know some of the basic rules. Together with one or two other students, try to list three important points in the space below. (Take about 5 minutes.)

Don't worry about getting them wrong!

1.

2.

3.

Compare your points with the following rules – if you got some right, well done. If not, make sure you know these for the future.

Some basic rules about lifting and carrying

- Never carry heavy objects a long distance. Find a trolley of some kind instead. Even a simple trolley makes carrying much easier.
- When lifting, keep your back straight, that is, "lift with the knees".

Figure 1

Start in a good posture

Figure 2

Keep the load close to the waist

- Keep the object close to your body, as in the diagram. An adult male shouldn't carry more than about 25 kg.
- Don't twist your body when carrying – it puts much more load onto your spine.
- Get a colleague to help if the load is too heavy.

One important source of information is the HSE (Health and Safety Executive), whose website is www.hse.gov.uk. The pictures in figures 1 and 2 are taken from its leaflet "Getting to grips with manual handling".

Using equipment safely (P1)

When working in an engineering environment, here are some basic rules to help you work safely and to protect yourself and others around you.

- **Keep your work space tidy.**
  This means clearing away all materials when you have finished, and putting tools back in their place. Not only does this make it easier to find the tools next time, it means that there is less chance of accidents – for example, by falling over something left on the floor.

- **Avoid working alone**
  If you are working on machinery, or up a ladder, then you need to think what happens if you have an accident. If there is someone else present, they can get help.

- **Put safety guards in place**
  Some machines (such as pillar drills, hydraulic presses) have safety guards. These must always be put in place before using the equipment.

- **Clamp workpiece**
  If drilling a piece of metal, make sure it is firmly clamped before drilling starts. Give the reason for doing this.

  Reason for clamping workpiece:

  _____

  _____

Activity 2

Give two more examples of safe working practice, first when drilling or machining, and second when fault finding on some 230 V ac electrical equipment.

Safe working when machining:

_____

_____

Safe working when fault finding on electrical equipment:

_____

_____

Personal and protective equipment (P2)

A range of PPE is available when carrying out engineering work, and you need to be able to select appropriate PPE for various tasks.

A few basic items are given in the table:

PPE item	When to use
Safety boots or shoes, with protective toe caps	If working with heavy, hard objects. A 2 kg piece of steel dropped onto your toes will probably cause a lot of pain, quite apart from any broken bones!
Goggles, safety spectacles or face shield	To protect the eyes against chemicals, dust or particles that could fly into the eye, such as when using acids or during machining processes such as drilling.
Gloves or gauntlets	If handling objects with rough or possibly sharp edges. Also for some hot work, such as soft soldering.
Rubber gloves	To prevent skin irritation or burns from corrosive liquids.
Helmets	When there is a risk of falling objects or of bumping head.

In the space at the bottom of the previous table, try to find one other item of PPE you might need for some type of engineering activity, and add this into the table.

PPE at Work Regulations 1992

The main requirement of the PPE at Work Regulations 1992 is that personal protective equipment is to be supplied free of charge and used at work wherever there are risks to health and safety that cannot be adequately controlled in other ways.

The regulations require that PPE :

*   is properly assessed before use to ensure it is suitable

*   is maintained and stored properly

*   is provided with instructions on how to use it safely

*   is used correctly by employees.

Activity 3

When working in an engineering environment, great care must always be taken to prevent harm to yourself and to your fellow workers due to contact with hazardous materials and substances. Hazardous materials are generally classified into seven main groups.

Complete the table in figure 3. Identify the hazardous substance indicated by the symbol shown. Try to find a typical example for each group. Some have been completed for you.

Figure 3

Symbol	Group	Example
	Corrosive	

	Harmful (chemicals dangerous to health)	
	Highly flammable	

	Oxidising agent (provides oxygen, so can lead to fires, explosions)	Oxygen, hydrogen peroxide
		X-rays or radioactive material

There are also a number of other signs that must be displayed in a workshop environment.

These are colour coded, and give either instructions or information. They are Red – "do not do", Blue – "must do", Yellow – "warning of potential danger", and Green – indicating a "safe condition" or the "safe way to do".

Activity 4

In pairs or small groups, have a good look around your school or college workshop. See how many different general safety signs you can find and record them in a table similar to the one shown below:

Colour	Meaning or purpose	Instruction/information

Compare your results with those of other groups.

Risk assessments

Risk assessments are done in order that the dangers in, say, a workshop or in carrying out some process can be worked out and written down.

The basic idea is simple – walk around the area, note any possible risks to anyone who may be in the area and talk to any other people involved. Then work out the right kind of precautions that need to be taken.

One sensible way to do this is to follow the "five steps to risk assessment" suggested by the HSE.

- Step 1: Identify the hazards

- Step 2: Decide who might be harmed, and how

- Step 3: Weigh up the risks and decide on precautions

- Step 4: Record your findings, and carry them out

- Step 5: Update the risk assessment as needed

These steps are outlined in more detail on the HSE website.

Example: Motor vehicle workshop

The HSE provides a number of examples on its website. Part of one of these is shown below. It is for the fire hazard in a motor vehicle workshop.

What are the hazards?	Who might be harmed and how?	What are you already doing?	What further action is necessary?	Action by whom and when	Done?
Fire	Building could be burnt down, workers and visitors could be trapped in burning building. Workers could suffer severe or fatal burns if petrol gets on them and is ignited.	Smoking prohibited in all work areas. Fire alarms maintained and tested by manufacturer. Extinguishers provided and inspected under contract. Special fire exits not needed as all work areas have immediate access to outside.	Manager to arrange some training on use of extinguishers for all workers. Annual fire drill to be carried out.	S B 10/6/2007 J D 20/1/2008	Yes Yes

Obviously there are other hazards, such as exhaust fumes, using an angle grinder, and the car lift ramp. But from this we can see that a risk assessment has been carried out using the five main steps referred to earlier.

Every company with more than five employees must have a written safety policy by law. The policy document will depend on the size and type of organisation. It could be quite simple for a small office, but would be much a much larger document for a big engineering company.

It should contain the following information:
- the person responsible for overall safety
- who undertakes risk assessments of the workshop, and how often.
- who carries out COSHH (Control of Substances Hazardous to Health) assessments
- how problems with equipment are reported
- location of the first-aid box
- name and location of the first aider for the workshop
- accident book location
- person responsible for fire procedures.

2   Using and Interpreting Engineering Information

This section provides an introduction to Unit 2, and covers the grading criteria P5 and M2.

However, it will be helpful to partly cover some of the other criteria (such as P1), so some extra information has been included.

Unit abstract for these criteria

- *Drawing and document care and control:*
  location and security eg storage conditions, access points and return procedures, reporting discrepancies in data and documents; physical handling eg damage and effects from graffiti, cleanliness, folding methods; document control eg issue and amendment dates, part/pattern numbers, reporting of loss/damage.

A brief explanation of what you need to do for each of the grading criteria covered in this guide is given in the following table:

Grading criteria	What do I need to do for this?
P5 describe the care and control procedures for the drawings and related documentation used when carrying out and checking own work output	This relates to the drawings and other documents used in criteria P1 to P4. You need to describe the way in which all these documents are handled when carrying out a task and say how they can be protected and kept in good condition. Reference should also be made to document control, for example, what happens if the document gets damaged.
M2 evaluate and identify improvements in the care and control procedures used for drawings and related documentation	Identify some ways of improving the care and control of documents. Evaluate the benefits of the methods identified.

The two criteria above do not tell you the actual types of drawings, documents and information involved in this unit: that is covered by the other grading criteria, P1 to P4 and M1.

It is useful therefore to look at the other criteria to see some of the key documents and drawings that may be needed.

3   Applied Electrical and Mechanical Science for Technicians

This section provides an introduction to Unit 3, and covers the grading criteria P1, P2, P3, M1 and D1.

Unit abstract for these criteria

1   **Be able to define and apply concepts and principles relating to electrical science**

Definitions of parameters of direct current: electrical charge; electric current; electromotive force; electrical resistance; electrical power.

Definitions of parameters of magnetic fields: magnetic fields; magnetic flux and flux density.

Direct current electrical circuits: circuit symbols; Ohm's Law; potential difference; current; resistance in series and parallel circuit networks; data for calculations.

Magnetic circuits: force on a current-carrying conductor; construction, function and use of electro-magnetic coils eg relays, contactors, solenoids, sensors, motors, transformers; data for calculations.

2   **Be able to define and apply concepts and principles relating to mechanical science**

Definitions of parameters of static and dynamic systems: mass; weight; force; moment of a force; density; relative density; displacement; velocity; acceleration; work; power.

A brief explanation of what you need to do for each of the grading criteria covered in this guide is given in the following table:

Grading criteria	What do I need to do for this?
P1 define parameters of direct current electricity and magnetic fields	Be able to define all the basic electrical parameters.
P2 determine total resistance, potential difference and current in series and parallel dc circuits from given data	Show how to calculate the total resistance of resistors in series and also in parallel. Find the current or voltage in these circuits.
P3 define parameters of static and dynamic mechanical systems	Be able to define all the basic mechanical parameters.
M1 determine the force on a current carrying conductor situated in a magnetic field from given data	… as stated!
D1 describe the basic construction, functioning and use of an electromagnetic coil.	Describe one of the main uses of an electromagnetic coil, such as a relay, transformer, contactor or motor.

Activity 1: Static electricity (P1)

Electrical charge

Tear up one or two small (3 to 5 mm) pieces of paper and put them on the table. Then rub a small Perspex rod, or just a pen made from a polymer, onto your hair, or your jumper.

When you put the pen near the pieces of paper, they should stick to the pen.

Figure 6

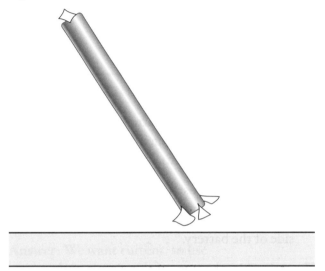

What happens is that when you rub an insulator, like Perspex, against hair, it becomes charged with static electricity. And charged objects can attract (or sometimes repel) other objects.

The amount of static (or stationery) charge is measured in coulombs, symbol capital C.

Definition: charge is a total quantity of electricity, measured in coulombs.

Electric current

A current of, say, 2 A through a wire, simply means 2 coulombs per second of charge is flowing.

Definition: electric current is the rate at which charge is flowing, measured in amperes (A). One ampere just means one coulomb per second. The word ampere is often abbreviated to amp.

Direct current (dc)

This just means a current that flows in one direction only. The most common example is current from a battery – this is dc.

The following sketch shows a circuit consisting of a small battery, a bulb and connecting wires. In this circuit the current flows one way only.

With an arrow, sketch the direction in which the current flows around the circuit.

Figure 7

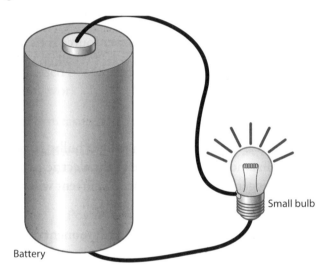

Battery   Small bulb

Electromotive force (EMF)

An EMF is just a voltage, but it refers to the voltage of a power source, such as a battery or the main electricity supply. (Strictly speaking it should be the voltage when there is no load connected to the battery, but provided the load is not too big, it makes little difference.)

Magnetism

People have been interested in magnets for hundreds of years, because of the way that two magnets can either attract each other, or repel each other. A simple bar magnet has a north pole end and a south pole end.

Figure 9

Even though it can't be seen, there is a magnetic field around the magnet that will, for example, attract small pieces of iron towards the magnet.

Activity 5

Sketch some lines around the magnet to show its magnetic field. (Note, if you have a bar magnet under a sheet of card and some iron filings on top of the card, you can "see" the effects of the magnetic field. You may need to tap the card gently.)

Definition: A magnetic field is the area around a magnet where a magnetic force exists on another magnet. The direction of a magnetic field is the direction in which a magnetic north pole will try to move. Use this information to put some arrows onto the lines.

The magnetic field of a bar magnet is strong close to one of its poles, but gets weaker as you move away. In order to get a strong magnetic field over a reasonable area, it has been found that using a horseshoe shape is better than a bar magnet.

Figure 10

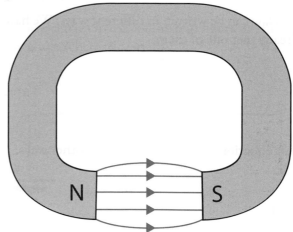

This is the system used in many electromagnetic machines, such as motors, generators andmoving-coil ammeters, because it produces a strong and reasonably constant field over a region.

Flux density (symbol B)

Definition: Flux density is the strength of a magnetic field at any point. It is measured in teslas, symbol capital T.

For example, the flux density of a strong magnet could be one or two teslas close to the poles of the magnet. The flux density of the Earth's magnetic field on the other hand is quite small, typically 0.0002 T.

Magnetic flux (symbol Φ)

This is the total amount of magnetic flux over a given area, A. It is measured in webers (Wb).

Definition: Magnetic flux is the flux density, B, multiplied by the area, A. In symbols:

$$\Phi = B \times A$$

Example: The flux density produced by a magnet is 0.3 T. If this is the flux density over an area of 0.6 m², find the total flux.

Using $\Phi = B \times A$
gives $\Phi = 0.3 \times 0.6 = 0.18$ Wb

Series and parallel circuits (P2)

These are two basic ways of connecting components, each one has its uses.

Series circuit

In this case the three components R1, R2 and R3 are connected as shown in figure 11.

(Note: for simplicity, only resistors are shown but they could be lamps, LEDs, buzzers or any other component.)

Figure 11

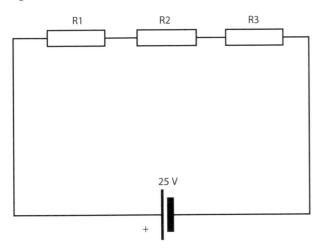

The electric current now has to pass through R1, R2 and R3 as well. This means that:

Total resistance = R1 + R2 + R3

Activity 6

- In a series circuit, there are three resistors of 20 Ω, 30 Ω and 50 Ω. What is the total resistance?

  Answer : Total resistance is _____ Ω

Current flow

It is important to know that in a series circuit, there is only **one** current, and it is the **same for all resistors.**

- If the battery voltage is 25 V, calculate the current flow through the resistors.

  Answer : Current is _____ A

Voltages across the resistors

The voltage (sometimes called the potential difference, or pd) across each resistor can easily be found now, by using $V = I \times R$ for each resistor in turn.

- Calculate the voltage across each resistor:

  Voltage across R1 (20 Ω) =

  Voltage across R2 (30 Ω) =

  Voltage across R3 (50 Ω) =

  Total of these voltages   =

If you have done this correctly, the total should be the battery voltage, 25 V! This is a way to check that your answer is OK.

The direction of the force: (left hand rule)

This can be found by holding the thumb, first finger and second finger of the LEFT hand all at right angles to each other. (Like the corner of a box.)

Then, if the First finger points in the direction of the Field, and the seCond finger in the direction of the Current, then the thuMb will be pointing in the direction of Motion.

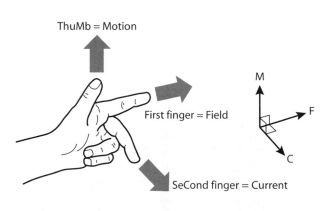

Note: if the conductor is parallel to the magnetic field, then the force on it is always zero.

Figure 17

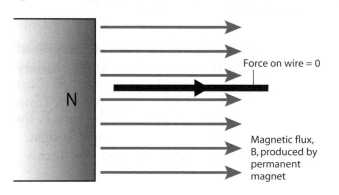

Applications

There are various devices and instruments that use this electromagnetic force. The most common one is the electric motor.

This uses a coil of wire, placed between the poles of a magnet, as shown in figure 18.

Figure 18

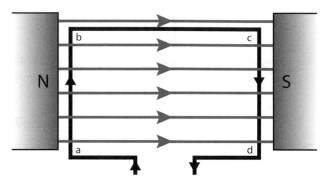

The rectangular loop of wire, abcd, is shown in red. Only the parts of it at right angles to the field will have a force on them: parts ab and cd.

The coil is wound onto a free rotating cylinder, placed in the middle of the field. To keep the field strong, the cylinder (not shown) is made from iron.

Activity 9

Work out the directions of the force on:

- Part ab: _____

- Part cd: _____

You should find that the forces are opposite to each other, which will cause the loop to rotate.

The only problem is that the wires leading the current into and out of the field will quickly get twisted up! The solution is to use a sliding contact system, called a commutator. (A commutator is just a metal ring, cut in half.)

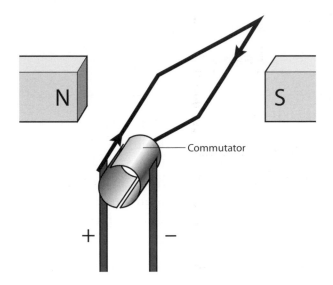

Moving coil meter

This is used to measure current, and is very similar to the electric motor.

The main difference is that the coil has a small spiral spring attached to it, so the coil can only rotate about a third of a complete turn before it stops. It can only do that if there is a strong current through it. If the current is very small, the coil may only turn through a few degrees before the force from the spring stops it turning any more. More details of the moving coil meter can be found in electrical textbooks, or by using a search engine.

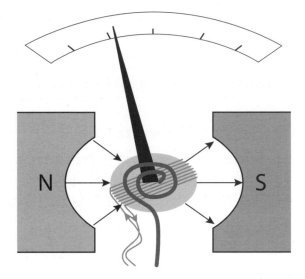

Relays

A relay is just a small electromagnet which, when energised, operates a switch. This switch is used to control a separate circuit, which usually has higher voltages or currents.

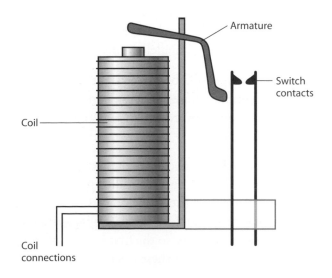

4   Mathematics for Engineering Technicians

This section provides an introduction to Unit 4, and covers the grading criteria P1, P2, P3, M1, M2 and D1.

P1 use mathematical methods to transpose and evaluate simple formulae

P2 determine the area of two regular shapes from given data

P3 determine the volume of two regular solid bodies from given data

M1 transpose and evaluate complex formulae

M2 identify the data required and determine the area of two compound shapes

D1 transpose and evaluate combined formulae

Unit abstract for these criteria

Transpose and evaluate: solution of problems that require the manipulation of simple equations including bracketed terms, roots and powers, eg:

$V = IR$, $P = VI$, $pV = c$, $v = u + at$, $s = \frac{1}{2}(u + v)t$, $P = I^2R$, $v = \sqrt{2gh}$, $I = \sqrt{(P/R)}$

complex formulae, eg:

$s = ut + \frac{1}{2}at^2$, $R\,v^2 = u^2 + 2as$, $V = V_o \sin 2\pi\,ft$, $Xc = 1/2\pi fC$

combining formulae, eg:

$\frac{1}{2}mv^2 = mgh$ find v, $\frac{1}{2}QV = \frac{1}{2}CV^2$ find V

Area: areas of regular shapes eg squares, rectangles, triangles, circles; area of compound shapes eg L-shapes, parallelograms.

Volume: regular solid bodies eg right rectangular prisms, cylinders, cones, spheres; compound solid bodies eg truncated prisms, cylinders with spherical ends.

Note: not included above are the basic operations in maths, such as addition and multiplication, and the use of powers of numbers and of brackets. You do need to be able to handle these basic operations, so the first section of this maths guide will cover these operations.

The BODMAS rule

This gives the order or sequence in which operations should be done.

For example, suppose we have to work out:

$$4 + 3 \times 2$$

Which operation should we do first – the addition or the multiplication? We get different answers, depending on which way we do it. (Check this yourself.)

In order that everybody gets the same result, it was decided to give multiplication the priority.

This means that the calculation becomes:

$$4 + 6 = 10$$

Activity 1

Use your calculator to work out $4 + 3 \times 2$ (key it in just as it's written). You will find that the calculator gives the right result (10). This is because the calculator has been programmed to do multiplications and divisions before it does the additions or subtractions.

Suppose we have a more complicated sum:

$$30 - (2 \times 3^2 + 5)$$

This is where we need the general rule, which is called "BODMAS". The letters stand for:

B: Brackets. Anything inside brackets must be worked out first.

O: Order. "Order" is an old word, not used these days. It really means powers like 3^2. This is said "three squared" (or "three to the power of two"). So any powers are worked out next. (This includes square roots – which are the same as a power.)

D: Division is done next.

M: Multiplication.

A: Addition.

S: Subtraction is done last.

(Perhaps this rule should nowadays be renamed BPDMAS)!

Communication & Learning Skills Module

Click here to enter you name

Click here to enter your Student Number

So taking the example $30 - (2 \times 3^2 + 5)$, we work out the brackets first. To do this, we use "ODMAS" as needed inside the brackets. So the power comes next, $3^2 = 9$.

Next do the multiplication, $2 \times 9 = 18$, then add 5 to finish off the brackets part. The result is that the number inside the brackets is 23. The brackets can now be removed.

So the calculation is now $30 - 23$ which is just 7.

Activity 2

- Repeat this calculation on your calculator, to make sure your calculator knows the rules!

- Work out $45 + (5 \times 10^2 - 100)$ from first principles, and then check with your calculator.

Powers of 10

These have a special place in maths and engineering. They make it easier to write numbers which are very large. For example, instead of 2,300,000,000 we can write: 2.3×10^9

Important note: most calculators can do this conversion automatically. But watch out – a calculator will show this number as 2.3^9. It expects you to know that it has missed out the "x 10" part, which should be between the 2.3 and the ^{9}.

With powers like 10^3, this simply means 10 multiplied by itself three times: $10 \times 10 \times 10$
A table of these powers of 10 is shown below. Fill in the missing gaps.

Power	Meaning	Actual number
10^4	10 × 10 × 10 × 10	10,000
10^3		
10^2	10 × 10	
10^1	10	10

The table can be extended to negative numbers as well.

Power	Meaning	Actual number
10^0	1	1
10^{-1}	1/10	0.1
10^{-2}	1/(10 × 10)	0.01
10^{-3}	1/(10 × 10 × 10)	

If you look at the patterns in both tables, you can see it makes some sense!
Again, your calculator "knows" that 10^{-3}, say, is really the same as 0.001.

The EXP key (used for powers of 10)

Powers of 10 happen quite often, so to save us time, most calculators have the special EXP key. When you press this, it means " $\times$ 10 to the power of".

So to key in 2.3×10^9, you enter "2.3" first, then hit the EXP key, and finally enter "9".

Note: do not press the "×" key!!!

Example 1

If you can get the correct answer to the following problem, then you are using the EXP key correctly:

$$1.5 \times 10^3 \times 2$$

The right answer is 3,000.

So get to know and trust your calculator.

Powers and prefixes in engineering

Some powers of 10, such as 10^3 have special names – kilo in this case, usually abbreviated to just "k". So 5000 m becomes 5 km.

The table below gives a list of the main prefixes:

Power	Prefix	Abbreviation	Example
10^9	giga	G	2 GΩ
10^6	mega	M	1.5 MV
10^3	kilo	k	4.7 km
10^{-3}	milli	m	5 mA
10^{-6}	micro	μ	25 μV
10^{-9}	nano	n	4 nm
10^{-12}	pico	p	10 pF

Note: anything with a minus power is a very small amount.

Transposition of formulae

Transposition means rearranging an equation, so that the thing you want to find is on one side of the equation only, and by itself.

Example 2

$a + 7 = 13$ Find a.

The basic principle of transposition is:

   Whatever you do to one side of the equation, you must do exactly the same to the other

So the equation will still be correct.

In this case we have a "7" on the left side which we want to get rid of.

The next principle is to "do the opposite" operation on the "7". The 7 is added, so to get rid of it, we subtract 7 from both sides:

$a + 7 - 7 = 13 - 7$

The equation is different, but it's still correct, because we took 7 from *both* sides.

This can now be simplified to: a = 6 (Answer)

Example 3

Suppose now the equation in example 2 had 3a (that is, three times a):

$$3a + 7 = 13$$

It's better to get rid of things that are added (or subtracted) first, just as with example 1. This gives:

$$3a = 6$$

Now we want to get rid of the "3" from the left side. The opposite operation in this case is to divide each side by 3 (because we have 3 multiplied by a to start with):

$$\frac{3a}{3} = \frac{6}{3}$$

On the left, the 3s will cancel out (multiply by three and divide by three, just leaves the "a" on its own). Then:

$$a = \frac{6}{3}$$

So a = 2 (Answer)

Powers

Example 4

$$\sqrt{(W + 1)} = 2.5$$

Note that a square root is a type of power. We can get rid of the square root on the left by squaring each side. (Or you can think of it as multiplying each side by itself.)

We are going to use the fact that, for example:

$$\sqrt{3} \times \sqrt{3} = 3$$

$$\sqrt{(W + 1)} \times \sqrt{(W + 1)} = 2.5 \times 2.5$$

This gives W + 1 = 6.25

Take 1 from each side:

W = 5.25 (Answer)

Example 5

If $V^2 + 1 = 26$, find V

The first task is to get rid of the "+ 1" by subtracting 1 from both sides:

$$V^2 + 1 - 1 = 26 - 1$$

Or
$$V^2 = 25$$

To find V, from V^2, we do the opposite of squaring. In this case it means find the square root:

$$\sqrt{V^2} = \sqrt{25}$$

Note: $\sqrt{V^2} = \sqrt{(V \times V)} = V$

So
$$V = 5 \quad \text{(Answer)}$$

Example 6

There are lots of equations which have three quantities in the same type of relationship, such as:

$$s = v\,t$$

$$V = I\,R$$

$$P = V\,I$$

You need to be able to transpose this sort of equation.

Suppose we have P = V I, and we want to find "I".

This means we need to get rid of the "V" on the right. At the moment V is multiplied by I, so to get rid of V we do the opposite – divide both sides by V:

$$\frac{P}{V} = \frac{VI}{V}$$

Now on the right side, if you multiply by V then divide by V, it just leaves "I":

$$\frac{P}{V} = I$$

You could leave the answer like this, but most people prefer to have the answer the other way round, with the single quantity you want on the left:

$$I = \frac{P}{V}$$

Combined formulae

These are ones where you can get the same quantity on both sides of the equation, such as:

$$I^2 R = V I$$

These are both formulae for electrical power.

Suppose you need to find R, say. The same approach is used.

First simplify the equation. If you see the same quantity on both sides of an equation, you can usually get rid of it on one side, at least.

In this equation, "I" appears on both sides. On the left it is I^2, but this is just $I \times I$.

Divide both sides by I, this will make things simpler:

$$\frac{I^2 R}{I} = \frac{V I}{I}$$

Now I^2 divided by I is just I. And on the right side of the equation, I divided by I = 1, which means that on the right side we have $V \times 1$, which is just V. So now the final result is:

$$I R = V$$

You may recognise this as Ohm's law, although we should finish it by writing $V = I R$.

Summary of transposing

- Do the same operation to both sides.
- The operation to do is the *opposite* of what's already there.

The only way to get the hang of this is to do lots of examples. Try some from your maths book. Or, if you enter "transpose equations" into a search engine, you'll find lots of examples, some easy, some hard.

Areas and volumes

Areas

Knowing how to calculate areas is useful – for example, if you want to buy carpet or any flooring. The price is usually quoted per square metre.

Area of a rectangle

This is a common shape, and the formula for the area is simply:

$$\text{Area} = \text{length} \times \text{height} \ (A = l \times h)$$

Figure 19

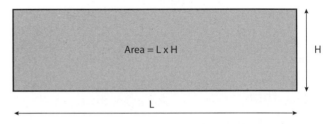

Units

The standard unit in engineering is square metres (m^2). Don't forget – always give the unit for an area.

Area of a parallelogram

Figure 20

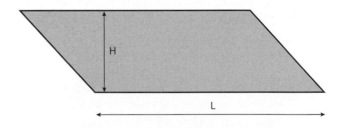

The formula is the same as that of a rectangle:

$$\text{Area} = \text{length} \times \text{height}$$

$$A = l \times h$$

To see that this is true, imagine cutting off the corner on the left, and moving it to the right: you end up with a simple rectangle.

Area of a triangle

The most common formula used is:

Area = ½ (length x height)

Figure 21

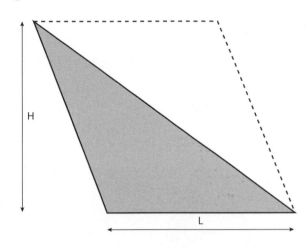

The area is half the area of the parallelogram shown with the dotted lines.

Activity 3

Find the area, in square metres, of the right angled triangle shown in figure 22.

Figure 22

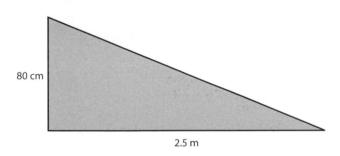

Area of a circle

The area of a circle is πr^2

Where $\pi = 3.142$

Figure 23

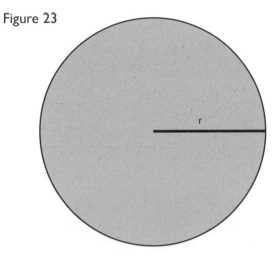

If the diameter is given, don't forget to halve it!

Compound shapes

Shapes are sometimes mixtures of squares, circles, etc. In this case, split the compound shape into some basic shapes, calculate their areas, and finally add them up.

Activity 4

A running track has the shape shown in figure 24, and the ends are semi-circular.

Figure 24

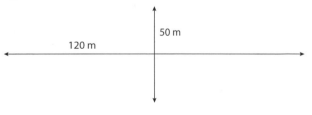

Find the total area enclosed by the track.

Volumes

Volume can be measured using a variety of units, although cubic metres (m³) is the standard engineering unit. But other common units are cc (cubic centimetres), litres, cubic feet, etc.

Volumes of solids

The most basic shape is a cubic type box.

Figure 25

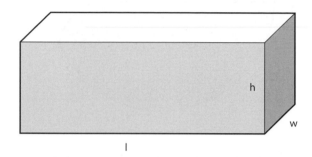

The volume is length × width × height. That is:

$$V = l \, w \, h$$

Solids with constant cross-section

These are solids like the ones shown in figure 26. They are called right prisms.

Figure 26

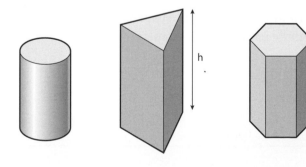

For these solids the volume is:

The area of the base multiplied by the height, h.

For example, for the middle solid, this would be the area of the triangle, multiplied by height h.

Activity 5

The diameter of a circular bar of metal is 0.1 m. Find the volume of a length of 0.5 m of this bar.

Hint: find the radius of the bar first, then calculate its cross-sectional area.

Volume of a cone

The cone has a circular base, and its height is h as shown in figure 27.

Figure 27

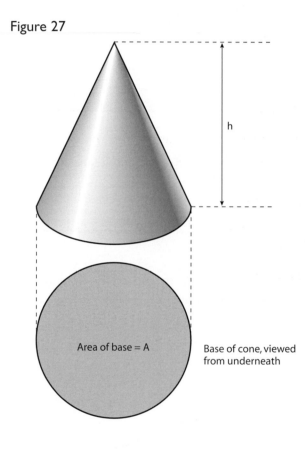

Area of base = A

Base of cone, viewed from underneath

The volume of the cone is:

$$\text{Volume} = \frac{1}{3} \times \text{area of base x height}$$

$$\text{Volume} = \frac{1}{3} \times Ah$$

Pyramids

The same formula applies to a pyramid, but with a pyramid the base is just a square.

Figure 28

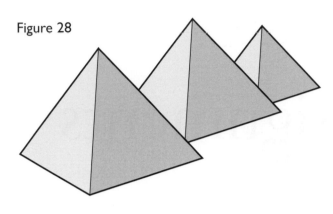

Activity 6

Find the volume of a pyramid, if its square base is 20 m × 20 m, and its height is 15 m.

Volume of a sphere

The sphere is the last basic shape you need to know.

Its volume is given by:

$$\text{Volume} = \frac{4}{3}\pi r^3$$

Compound shapes

Compound shapes have to be broken down into simpler shapes, in order to find their volume.

For example, suppose we have a cylinder of length l, which has a spherical end – a section through it is shown in figure 29. The radius of the cylinder and the radius of the hemisphere are the same, that is, "r".

Figure 29

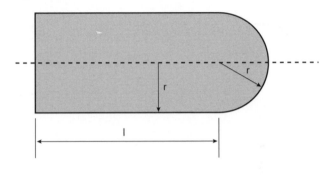

The total volume is:

Volume = volume of cylinder + ½ the volume of a sphere, radius "r"

Try to work out the formula for this shape.

Marked assignments

Exemplar assignment

Unit 1 – Working Practices in Engineering

Assignment 1.1: Safety, PPE and Identify Risks

Grading criteria covered: P1, P2 and P3

The following assignment is an example of the work you will need to do to achieve the pass criteria P1, P2 and P3.

(You will find one student's completed assignment following after the tasks.)

Task A (P1)

i) There are some 2 m lengths of angle iron stored in a rack in the workshop. They are low carbon steel, with a thickness of 3 mm, and 40 mm × 40 mm section. You are required to safely make a simple bracket out of a length of this angle iron. The final product should have four 10 mm holes in it, and be 65 mm in length as indicated in the sketch. Each hole is centred 20 mm from an end.

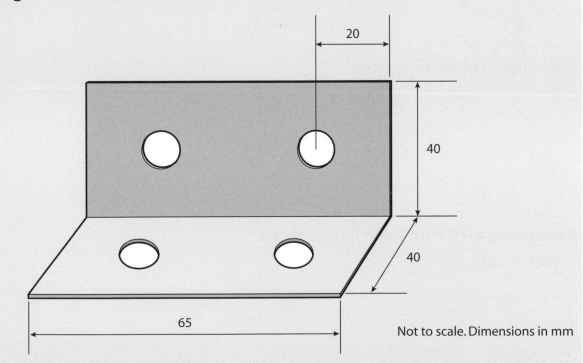

20

40

40

65

Not to scale. Dimensions in mm

You should carry out this task under the supervision of your teacher. Make a few notes on each part of the task, and your teacher will witness that you have carried out each part safely.

Fetching the 2 m length:

Your notes:

Witness statement:

Cutting off a 65 mm length:

Your notes:

Witness statement:

Producing a 10 mm hole in the steel:

Your notes:

Witness statement:

ii) Identify the seven main groups of hazardous substances by labelling the symbols below.

Task B (P2)

You need to record the PPE equipment that you selected and used for task A.

Choose three processes, such as sawing, that you carried out in task A, and then complete the following table. Obtain a witness statement from your teacher that describes how you selected and used the PPE equipment.

Process	PPE equipment selected and used	Witness

Witness statement:

Task C (P3)

For this, you must identify the hazards and risks that are associated with Task A. The following note will help with this task.

Note: Hazards and Risks

A hazard is something that can be dangerous, or cause some harm, such as split oil on a floor, a damaged electrical cable, chemicals, noise, etc.

A risk is the harm that can be caused to someone, such as a fall, burns, eye damage, etc.

In all cases, we must make sure that the risk, or chance of causing harm, is as low as possible, for example by clearing up any spilt oil, or by replacing damaged cables.

For this task, list four hazards that could be harmful, in making the bracket in Task A. Try to indicate the level of risk as high or low.

Hazard	Risk
1	
2	
3	
4	

Jason Burns: Assignment 1.1

Task A i) (P1)

Fetching the 2 m length:

Your notes

The steel to be cut was quite long and heavy, so I got Sharon to help me carry it to the workbench. I put it in the vice, while Sharon held the other end. I then measured off the length of just over 65 mm, to allow for filing down.

I wore gloves when carrying the piece of steel, and sawing it, as the ends had some sharp edges.

Witness statement:

Good. Jason and Sharon took the steel out carefully – ensuring that pathway was clear. They also replaced it carefully when they had finished.

Cutting off a 65 mm length:

Your notes:

I kept the cut piece in the vice and then used a hacksaw to cut it off to the marked length. I then used a file to remove the sharp edges.

Sharon then cut her piece, and afterwards we brushed up the filings to leave the workbench clean, and put the tools back on the toolrack.

Witness statement:

Jason and Sharon worked well together – Sharon made sure the steel did not fall down, at the point when Jason had just sawn through the steel.

Producing a 10 mm hole in the steel:

Your notes:

I marked out the hole centres with a scribe, and then used a centre punch and small hammer to mark the 4 centres clearly.

I took the bracket to the pillar drill, and decided to drill a small pilot hole, with a 2 mm drill bit first.

The bit was securely fastened into the chuck, and I made sure I took the chuck key out afterwards.

I placed the bracket into a clamp, with piece of wood under the bracket, so that when the drill went through, it would only cut into the wood, and not into the clamp. Wearing safety goggles, and with the drill guard down also, I switched on the drill and brought the bit down so it went right through the steel. I switched off the drill, and replaced the bit with a 10 mm one, and repeated the drilling process.

I did this for the other 3 holes, and afterwards used a small file to get rid of a few burrs around the holes.

When finished, I cleaned up and replaced the bits in their holder.

Witness statement:

Jason – you did not really need to use the wooden piece, you could have clamped the bracket so that the drill would just come through the bracket without hitting the clamp. Also you could have drilled ALL the 2 mm holes first!

But overall, the equipment was handled safely, and tidying up procedure was followed.

The hole positions and dimensions were as per the specification.

Task A ii) (P1)

Identify the seven main groups of hazardous substances by labelling the symbols below.

The seven groups, in order are:

 1. Corrosive

 2. Explosive

 3. Harmful to health

 4. Oxidising agents

 5. Toxic

 6. Highly flammable

 7. Radiation / Radioactive hazard

P1 awarded

Task B (D1)

The college, its staff and students have responsibilities to ensure that everyone working or visiting the workshop can do this safely.

The person responsible for overall safety	Mr R Wilson Room 203A, tel extension 3044
Who undertakes risk assessments of the workshop, and how often.	Mr R Wilson Room 203A
Who carries out COSHH (Control of Substances Hazardous to Health) assessments	Dr A Baxter, Room 210
How problems with equipment are reported	To the technician in charge
Name and location of the first aider for the workshop	Mrs D Brown, Room 206B
Location of the first-aid box	By the main door of the workshop, room 203
Accident book location	In the technician's room, 203A
Person responsible for fire procedures	Mr A Jones, Head of Department, room 225

D1 not achieved

Feedback

Jason – what you have shown is correct, even though you have just taken the headings from the notes given earlier. However, you have made no reference at all to legislation that is relevant to the actual work area. You should also give the telephone numbers of all the people mentioned in safety policy.

Exemplar assignment

Unit 2 – Using and Interpreting Engineering Information

Assignment 2.1: Document care and control procedures
Grading criteria covered: P5 and M2

This assignment will depend on the task carried out for the other grading criteria, mainly P1. Let's suppose this task was to carry out a modification to a piece of equipment in a workshop. To fix our ideas, suppose it was to replace a faulty push-button switch on a lathe.

Task A (P5)

You will need to locate the mechanical and electrical diagrams for the lathe. (These would be needed to find out how to get access to the switch, and to find the right type of replacement switch.)

Describe how the diagrams or documents are obtained, where they are stored, any security relating to them and general handling procedures.

You should carry out this task under the supervision of your teacher. Make a few notes on each part of the task, and your teacher will witness that you have carried out each part safely.

Task B (M2)

Identify some ways of improving the care and control of the documents used. Evaluate the benefits of the methods identified.

Other security measures

To improve security, it would be better for the filing cabinet to be kept locked. Also, when you return diagrams and sign the book, it would be better if someone else had to see you do it – you could sign the book, but not put the drawings back.

It might help if there was an instruction on the front "Keep these drawings clean, and away from liquids. Do not use on dirty bench tops."

One other improvement could be an extra "comments" part in the book, where you could report any damage that might be done.

M2 awarded

Feedback

Some useful points – you have got the right idea. I may mention these points to Mr Wilson!

Exemplar assignment

Unit 3 – Applied Electrical and Mechanical Science for Technicians

Assignment 3.1: Definitions of engineering terms
Grading criteria covered: P1, P2, P3, M1 and D1

Task 1 (P1)

Give a definition of the following terms, making sure that the appropriate **unit** (where needed) is also stated:

- Electrical charge
- Electric current
- EMF
- Electrical resistance
- Electrical power
- Magnetic field
- Magnetic flux
- Flux density

Task 2 (P2)

- A battery of 6 V is connected to a series circuit, consisting of a 9 Ω resistor and 15 Ω resistor.

  Draw this circuit. Find the total resistance, and the current flow provided by the battery. Use this to find the potential difference (voltage) across each resistor.

  Check your answer by adding the two voltages: the result should be the same as the supply voltage (or very close to it, if you have rounded off any of the numbers).

- The same resistors are now connected in parallel to the same 6 V battery. Draw this circuit.

  Calculate the total resistance of the circuit, and use this to find the total current supplied by the battery.

  Determine the potential difference across each resistor.

  Now use Ohm's law on each resistor separately, to calculate the current flow through each resistor.

  Check your results: the sum of the two currents should be the same as the current supplied by the battery.

Task 3 (P3)

Give a definition of the following terms, making sure that the appropriate **unit** (where needed) is also stated:

- Mass
- Weight
- Force
- Moment of a force
- Density
- Relative density
- Displacement
- Velocity
- Acceleration
- Work
- Power

Task 4 (M1)

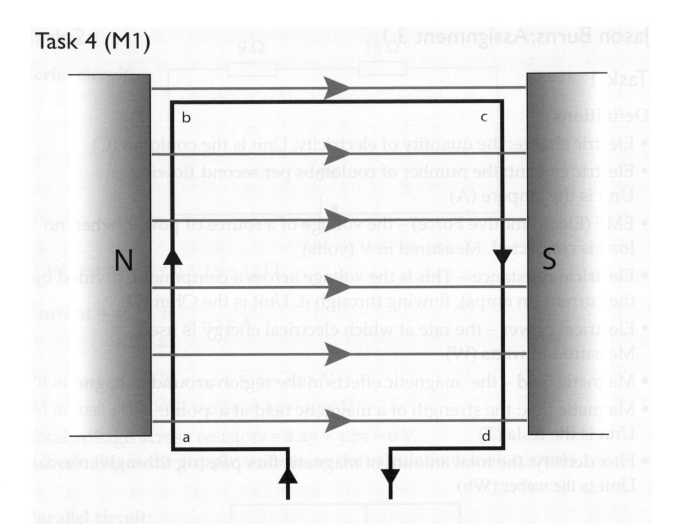

The dimensions of the conductors in the motor shown in the diagram are:

ab = cd = 25 cm

bc = 15 cm

The magnetic flux density, B = 0.4 T

If the current through the wire is 0.2 A, calculate the force on section:

- bc of the conductor
- ab of the conductor

Calculate the moment of the force on ab, about the centre of the coil.

Task 5 (D1)

Electromagnetic coils are used in all sorts of equipment. Describe the basic construction, operation and use of **one** electromagnetic coil.

Jason Burns: Assignment 4.2

Task 1

For P2:

1. The area of this is half the area of a circle = ½ × 3.142 × 900
                                    = 1414 mm²

2. The area is ½ bh = 0.5 × 15.3 × 2.7 = 20.7 m²

For M2:

3.

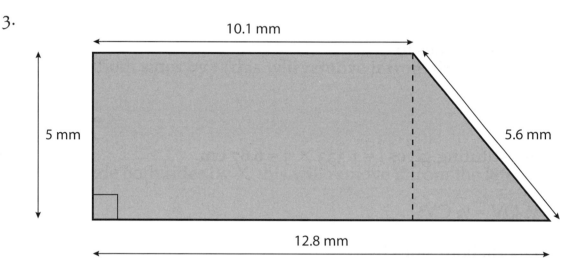

I split this shape into a rectangle and a right angled triangle, as shown with the dotted line.

From the data given, the base of the triangle is 12.8 – 10.1 = 2.7

The total area is = area of rectangle + area of triangle

= 10.1 × 5 + ½ × 2.7 × 5

= 50.5 + 6.75

= 57.25 mm²

4.

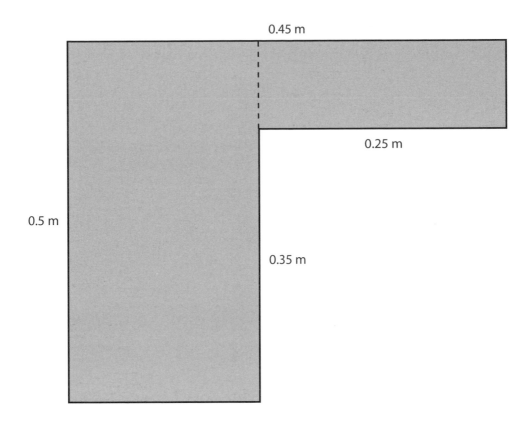

I spilt this into two rectangles with the dotted line shown.

From the data given, the large rectangle is 0.5 × (0.45 − 0.25)

So its area is 0.5 × 0.2 = 0.1 m²

The small rectangle is 0.25 × (0.5 − 0.35)

So its area is 0.25 × 0.15 = 0.0375 m²

The total area is 0.1375 m²

M2 awarded

Feedback

Well done Jason.